# CONTENTS

## A  Warm-up

(1) Write a sentence using these words only.

**moon the landed The rocket on**

_____

Put the letters in order to make two words.

(2) **t h e a** _____ and _____

(3) **a e m n** _____ and _____

Write a question using these words.

(4) **bears  honey**

_____

(5) **trees  winter**

_____

Add the missing letters.  **_Clue: days of the week_**

(6) M _ n d _ y

(7) S _ t _ rd _ y

(8) W _ dn _ sd _ y

(9) Th _ rsd _ y

(10) T _ _ sd _ y

## B  Word work

Write two compound words starting with **every**.

(1) every _____

(2) every _____

Write three words that mean the same as the word in **bold**.

(3) **little** house _____

(4) I was **happy**. _____

Underline the word that is wrongly spelt.
Write the correct spelling.

(5) The king frownd. _____

(6) The crowd gaspt. _____

(7) Clouds floatid by. _____

Add the same suffix.

(8) direc _____

(9) posi _____

(10) rota _____

## C  Sentence work

(1) Write this message using the word **and** only once.

We went to the city farm and we saw a baby lamb and he was lovely.

_____

(2) Circle the four capital letters.   On Saturday I saw Molly in town.

Write down why each capital letter was used.

(3) _____

(4) _____

(5) _____

(6) _____

Use the words to make a question.

(7) Jack did win. _____

(8) I can do that. _____

(9) They will come. _____

(10) You must go. _____

X There is only one correct answer.   X There is more than one correct answer.

## A  Warm-up

1  Write a sentence using these words.

**dog  duck**

Use these words to make four compound nouns.

**spoon  pot  cake  pan  tea  dust**

2  _____    4  _____

3  _____    5  _____

Put the words into rhyming pairs.
Add another rhyming word.

**break  great  day  shake  grey  late**

6  _____ , _____  and _____

7  _____ , _____  and _____

8  _____ , _____  and _____

9  Put these words in order to make a statement.

**you I that help with can**

10  Make a question using the same words.

## B  Word work

Add the correct plural ending.

1  short ____

2  jean ____

3  sunglass ____

Write the meaning of the word in **bold**.

4  The monster's face was **hideous**.

'hideous' means _____

5  The water **glistened** in the sun.

'glistened' means _____

6  The car had been **abandoned**.

'abandoned' means _____

Write four words that start with **ph**.

7  ph _____

8  ph _____

9  ph _____

10  ph _____

## C  Sentence work

What punctuation mark is hidden by the symbol?

I have my pencil■ ruler■ crayons and book▲

1  ▲  _____

2  ■  _____

3  Add four items to complete the sentence.

I went shopping and I bought _____

Change the nouns in **bold** to make a new sentence. Write the new sentence.

4  A **cloud** floated in the **sky**.

5  **James** dropped the **jelly**.

6  A **cat** crept through the **grass**.

Write whether the sentence is in the past tense or present tense.

7  Ella smiles at me. _____

8  I saw Rajesh. _____

9  We were playing. _____

10  She is waiting outside. _____

X There is only one correct answer.    X There is more than one correct answer.

5

## A  Warm-up

1. Write a sentence using these words only.

   **shook the girl her head little**

   _____

The same letter is missing from all these words.
Write it in.

2. ___ r e c k        4. ___ r o n g
3. ___ r i g g l e    5. ___ r i n k l e

Write two more words that start with the same
first two letters.

6. _____

7. _____

Write the pairs of words with the same spelling
pattern. Add another rhyming word.

**brother  would  another  could**

8. _____ , _____ and _____

9. _____ , _____ and _____

10. Write a question with these words in it.

    **elephant  trunk**

    _____

## B  Word work

Underline the correct spelling.

1. peeple   peopel   people   peepul

2. frute   fruit   froot   friut

3. ownly   only   onley   onlly

Write two words that mean the same as the word
in **bold**.

4. **cold**   _____  _____

5. **fast**   _____  _____

6. **old**    _____  _____

7. **sad**    _____  _____

Write three words that start with **ch** when it sounds
as it does in the name **Chris**.

8. _____

9. _____

10. _____

## C  Sentence work

Read this aloud.    **the rain poured down everyone was soaked the picnic was ruined**

1. How many sentences did you hear?  _____

2. Write the sentences with full stops and capital letters.

   _____

Add **but** or **so**.

3. He found the door _____ it was locked.      5. It is cold _____ it is not raining.

4. He found the door _____ he could escape.    6. It is cold _____ wrap up warm.

Write the sentence in the past tense.

7. This week, we go on holiday. Last week, _____.

8. Today it is raining. Yesterday _____.

9. The dragon snarls. Then _____.

10. Complete the sentence and add any punctuation marks that are missing.

    Inside  the  chest  there  was  a  magic  mirror  thirty  coins  a  string  of  beads

    and _____

Ⓧ There is only one correct answer.    Ⓧ There is more than one correct answer.

## A   Warm-up

Write six sentences using these words only.
Use three words in each sentence.

**he   we   they   was   were   happy   cold**

1. _____

2. _____

3. _____

4. _____

5. _____

6. _____

Write a word that sounds the same and uses the same letters.

7. bear and _____

8. brake and _____

Use these words to make two compound nouns.

**fly   green   house**

9. _____

10. _____

## B   Word work

Add the missing syllable.   *Clue: colours*

1. scar _____   3. em _____ ald

2. bur _____ dy   4. vi _ let

5. The same letter is missing from all these words. Write it in.

w _ sp      w _ nd      w _ d

Write the meaning of the word in **bold**.

6. a woodland **habitat**
   a 'habitat' is _____

7. Flowers **produce** seeds.
   'produce' means _____

8. Fruit **contains** seeds.
   'contains' means _____

Underline the word that is wrongly spelt. Write the correct spelling.

9. The giant had jinger hair. _____

10. The surfase was icy. _____

## C   Sentence work

Add the missing punctuation and capital letters.

1. I watched the match last night did you see it

2. ben ella samir megan and sarika were in my group

3. did you hear about ryan he broke his arm

Cross out the word that is wrong. Write the correct word.

4. The woman strided along. _____

5. The wind blowed. _____

6. We all weared our PE kit. _____

Add a phrase to these sentences to say **where** each event happened.

7. We saw the car _____

8. A plane landed _____

9. The man hid _____

10. Write a statement using these words.
    **tadpole – young frog**
    _____

X There is only one correct answer.      X There is more than one correct answer.

## A  Warm-up

Write a sentence using these words.

1  **dog  roof**

_____

2  **Gran  sunglasses**

_____

_____

3  **animal  motorway**

_____

_____

Add the missing letters.  **ir  er  ur  or**

4  t h ___ s t
6  w ___ m

5  s ___ p r i s e
7  p ___ s o n

Make three questions.

8  _____ is your name

9  _____ do you live

10  _____ old are you

## B  Word work

Make six words using these words and prefixes only.

**able  like  please  well  un  dis**

Write the word beside its meaning.

1  _____  ill or sick

2  _____  annoy or upset

3  _____  put out of action

4  _____  hate

5  _____  not able to do something

6  _____  different

Underline the correct spelling.

7  brushis  brushes  brushs

8  ladys  ladyes  ladies

These words have the same spelling pattern.

**giggle  puddle  wobble  drizzle**

9  What is the pattern?

_____

10  Write two words that end with **dge**.

_____ d g e  _____ d g e

## C  Sentence work

1  Add three items.  In my sandwich I had _____

Write an ending for the sentence.

2  We left early but _____

3  We must leave early or _____

Underline the verb.

4  Lizards eat insects.

5  Tigers hunt at night.

6  Hummingbirds hover near flowers.

7  Chimps swing through trees.

Add capital letters and full stops.

8  the  wind  turned  icy  lucy  shivered  she  hated  the  cold

9  it  was  getting  late  mr  brown  frowned  and  looked  at  his  watch

10  mark  lay  in  bed  he  listened  for  a  moment  it  all  seemed  quiet

8

## A Warm-up

Put the words into rhyming pairs.
Add another rhyming word.

**square  fear  door  sphere  more  bear**

(1) _____ , _____ and _____

(2) _____ , _____ and _____

(3) _____ , _____ and _____

(4) Change the nouns to make a new sentence.

Butter is made from cream.

_____ is made from _____ .

Make six sentences using some of these words only.

**I  she  we  is  are  am  brave  late**

(5) _____

(6) _____

(7) _____

(8) _____

(9) _____

(10) _____

## B Word work

Write these verbs so they end with **ing**.

(1) drum _____

(2) hook _____

(3) spit _____

(4) whirl _____

(5) bob _____

(6) scrape _____

Write these sentences with all the words
spelt correctly.

(7) We wotcht the swons and swollows.

(8) Her dad werks all over the werld.

Sort the verbs into two groups.

**amble    dart    dash    plod**

**trudge    sprint    saunter    tear**

(9) **run** _____

(10) **walk** _____

## C Sentence work

Write a sentence using these words.

(1) **bark and cat** _____

(2) **home but road** _____

(3) **gold or cave** _____

Add a verb in the past tense.

(4) The man _____ in a puff of smoke.

(5) They all _____ happily ever after.

(6) The door _____ open.

Write the sentence, adding the missing apostrophe.

(7) I put Dads gloves in his pocket.

(8) It must be Adams turn now.

(9) Is this a statement or a command? **Take it away.**

(10) Give a reason for your answer.

X There is only one correct answer.    X There is more than one correct answer.

9

## A  Warm-up

1  All the words have the same letters missing.
Write them in.

**ar  er  or  ir  ur**

w ___ t h          w ___ s e

w ___ k e r        w ___ s h i p

Write a question using these words only.

2  **is it dark night why at**

_____

3  **fizzy lemonade is why**

_____

Add **un** or **dis** to make a new word.

4  ___ trust          6  ___ selfish

5  ___ happy          7  ___ agree

Add the missing letters.

*Clue: found in the body*

8  h ___ r t

9  s ___ l ___ t

10  l ___ g s

## B  Word work

1  Underline the three words that mean the same
as **looked**.

glanced  glared  nudged  peered  jerked

Add a suffix to make the word into a noun.

2  amaze ___

3  foolish ___

4  treat ___

Make the noun into a plural.

5  one dish        → three ___

6  one plate       → three ___

7  one lunchbox    → three ___

8  one glass       → three ___

Add the same suffix to all three words.

9  hope ___        pain ___        wish ___

10  smooth ___      kind ___        sudden ___

## C  Sentence work

Cross out the verb and use one of these instead. Write the verb in the correct tense.

**collapse  swagger  heave**

1  He puts the sack onto his back.          _____

2  The bridge was falling.                  _____

3  The pirate went down the road.           _____

Add a question mark or an exclamation mark to the end of the sentence.

4  Look out ___

5  What a fascinating fact ___

6  Why does the wind blow ___

7  Can I help ___

8  Whose shoes ___

9  Stop, thief ___

10  Complete this sentence.

The soil was so dry that _____

X  There is only one correct answer.      X  There is more than one correct answer.

## A   Warm-up

1   Change the nouns to make a new statement.

All elephants have trunks.

Add the missing letters.   *Clue: months*

2   N _ v _ m b _ r     4   J _ n _ _ r y

3   S _ p t _ m b _ r     5   F _ b r _ _ r y

Make four adjectives out of these words and suffixes.

**less   ful   fear   power**

6                 8

7                 9

10   Write two sentences. Use one of these words in each.

**cake   mess**

## B   Word work

Write the meaning of the word in **bold**.

1   Suddenly someone **yanked** my arm.

'yanked' means

2   The king was well **protected**.

'protected' means

Cross out the words that are wrongly spelt. Write the correct spellings.

3   Trains can traval through tunnuls.

4   Use the handel to lift the kettel.

5   He reached the finul and won a medel.

Write the verb with the **ed** ending added.

6   **train**

7   **trot**

8   **snap**

9   **stare**

10   **cry**

## C   Sentence work

Write a noun in each space to complete the sentence.

1   Three _____ were sitting on the old _____ by the _____ in the farmyard.

2   From the beach we could see _____ bobbing in the _____ near the _____ .

3   In the supermarket, a _____ with a _____ was standing by the _____ .

Write the sentence as an exclamation.

4   That is a lovely dress.

5   It is amazing.

6   It is a beautiful day.

Add the capital letters.

7   on saturday i went to see manchester city play aston villa.

8   on sunday i went to simon's house in west burton.

Complete the sentence.

9   Ice-cream starts to melt when

10   Water freezes when

X There is only one correct answer.    X There is more than one correct answer.    11

## A  Warm-up

Use the same letters to make a different word.

1. **quite** _____
2. **angle** _____

3. Write a sentence using these words.

   **cupboard  but  empty**

   _____

   _____

4. Add four nouns to complete the sentence.

   In the garden we saw beetles, _____

   _____

Write four nouns that start with **kn**.

5. _____     7. _____
6. _____     8. _____

Add the missing letters.

9. n o s t _ _ _     *Clue: part of a nose*
10. p u _ _ _      *Clue: part of an eye*

## B  Word work

1. What spelling rule do these words follow?

   **snagged  spinner  spotty  dragging**

   _____

   _____

   _____

Add one of the endings to these words.

2. knit _____     3. wrap _____

Write three nouns that name types of

4. **shop** _____ , _____ , _____
5. **road vehicle** _____ , _____
6. **dog** _____ , _____
7. **sportswear** _____ , _____ , _____

Add the correct prefix. Then write the meaning of the new word.

**un  dis**

8. _____ trust    means _____
9. _____ pack    means _____
10. _____ popular  means _____

## C  Sentence work

Cross out the verb **came** and use one of these verbs instead. Use the same tense.

**swarm  slither  trickle**

1. Water came out of the pipe.        _____
2. The ants came out of the hole.      _____
3. The snake came across the floor.     _____

Add the correct punctuation mark at the end of the line.

4. **Mum:** Shall we have beans for tea _____
5. **Child:** NO _____
6. **Mum:** But you like beans on toast _____
7. **Child:** No, I don't _____
8. **Mum:** Well, what about spaghetti then _____

Finish the sentence.

9. Goldilocks ran away because _____
10. Little Bear was angry because _____

X There is only one correct answer.   X There is more than one correct answer.

## A   Warm-up

Put the words into rhyming pairs.
Add another rhyming word.

**burn   noun   worth   drown   learn   earth**

1  _____ ,   _____ and _____

2  _____ ,   _____ and _____

3  _____ ,   _____ and _____

Write a statement, a question and an exclamation using the word **spaceship**.

4  **statement** _____

_____

5  **question** _____

6  **exclamation** _____

Add the missing vowels.

*Clue: numbers*

7  s _ v _ n t _ _ n

8  f _ _ r t _ _ n

9  _ l _ v _ n

10  _ _ g h t _ _ n

## B   Word work

Add to each sentence a verb ending with **ing**.

1  Ducks were _____ about on the water.

2  Ed was _____ the branch behind him.

3  The man is _____ his head in agreement.

4  I felt you _____ my shoulder.

Write the words as one word using an apostrophe.

5  **we have** _____

6  **I am** _____

7  **is not** _____

Write two words to use instead of **said** which could show that a person was

8  **speaking loudly** _____

9  **speaking quietly** _____

10  **speaking happily** _____

## C   Sentence work

Complete the sentence with an interesting noun phrase.

1  The king waited in _____

2  The fisherman waited in _____

3  The businessman hurried into _____

4  The actor hurried into _____

Finish the sentence.

5  The post office was closed when _____

6  The post office was closed so _____

7  The post office was closed because _____

Add the capital letters and punctuation.

8  it began to snow soft flakes gently landed on sarahs hair

9  suddenly there was a loud sound boom what was it

10  what is your favourite sort of dog is it a poodle a greyhound a collie or a bulldog

X There is only one correct answer.   X There is more than one correct answer.

13

## A  Warm-up

Finish the sentence.

1 Dogs bark when _____

2 I feel happy when _____

Read the words aloud. Underline the odd one out.

3 whisper   while   whole   whistle

4 Give a reason for your choice.

_____

_____

Add the missing letters.  *Clue: sports*

5 a t h ___ t ___ s

6 b a d ___ t ___ n

7 g ___ m n ___ t ___ s

8 s w ___ i n g

Write a statement and a question using these words only.

**swim  can  bears  polar**

9 **statement** _____

10 **question** _____

## B  Word work

1 What spelling rule do these words follow?

**spies  parties  stories  cities**

_____

Write two more words that follow the same rule.

2 _____

3 _____

4 The same letter is missing from all these words. Write it in.

s q u ___ s h      s w ___ p      w ___ n d e r

Write two verbs that mean the same as

5 **jump** _____

6 **shine** _____

Add a prefix and a suffix.

**un  dis  ful  ly**

7 ___ fair ___

8 ___ like ___

9 ___ help ___

10 ___ trust ___

## C  Sentence work

Add a verb to complete the sentence. Use the past tense of the verb.

**hunt  hurl  hurtle  huddle**

1 Adam _____ his toys away.

2 Our dog Ziggy _____ into the lake.

3 Lucy _____ by the fire to keep warm.

4 Deepak _____ for his rucksack.

Underline the nouns.

5 The boys packed tents, sleeping bags and a powerful torch.

6 What type of word is **powerful** in the sentence above? Tick one.    adjective __    adverb __

7 Change the nouns and noun phrases to make a new sentence.

The _____ packed _____

Write the sentence correctly.

8 Nina tom and sacha lives on george street

9 I red two book last week what about you

10 He was late getting too Ninas party

X There is only one correct answer.    X There is more than one correct answer.

## A Warm-up

Add a verb to complete the sentence.

1. The car _____ suddenly.

2. Everyone _____ happily.

3. The same ending is missing from all these words. Write it in.

   jock _____    troll _____    vall _____

Add a prefix and a suffix.

4. _____ usual _____    _____ grate _____

5. Look at how these words end.
   Underline the odd one out.

   double   label   table   bubble

6. Add the correct ending to these words.

   squirr _____    sizz _____    stap _____

Write four compound nouns that start with **eye**.

7. _____    9. _____

8. _____    10. _____

## B Word work

Write the meaning of the word in **bold**.

1. It was not what he **intended**.

   'intended' means _____

2. She was **irritated** by my remark.

   'irritated' means _____

3. He **trudged** back up the hill.

   'trudged' means _____

Add **un** or **dis** to make new verbs.

4. _____ own    6. _____ tie

5. _____ fold   7. _____ infect

8. What spelling rule do these words follow?

   **baker  striding  sparkled  shiny**

   _____

Write two more examples of words following this rule.

9. _____    10. _____

## C Sentence work

1. Underline the nouns in the sentence below.

2. Then draw a ring round the verbs.

   **The seagulls squawked loudly as the waves crept across the sand.**

3. What adverb is used in the sentence above? _____

Change the nouns and verbs so that the sentence describes

4. **a wood**    The _____ loudly as the _____ across the _____ .

5. **a street**  The _____ loudly as the _____ across the _____ .

Finish the sentence so that it says **when** the event happened.

6. Kerry woke up _____

7. They ran outside to play _____

8. We piled into the car _____

Complete the sentence.

9. I will need my umbrella if _____

10. She asked the man if _____

**Now complete Section 1 of the Progress chart on page 46.**

X There is only one correct answer.    X There is more than one correct answer.

15

## Sam gets lost

You are writing a story about Sam. He went out for the day with his family, but then he got lost. Write the part of the story when he realised he was lost. The first sentence is given. Describe what Sam saw and how he felt.

### Hints

Before you start:

- choose a setting
- think about the event
- imagine what Sam saw and heard
- consider how Sam felt
- make a note of words or ideas to use.

As you write, think about:

- the words you choose
- the sentences you write.

Sam looked around.

### Check

- When you have finished, check through your writing.
- Check that everything sounds right.
- Proofread to check spelling and punctuation.
- Make changes to improve it.

## My camping diary

Proofread this diary entry.

Change anything that does not look or sound correct.

### Hints

- Check that everything is clear and sounds right.
- Check that the punctuation and capital letters are correct.
- Check that the spelling is correct.

we arrivd at camp on sataday. I was shareing a tent with ben adam and Harvey. Mick was unnable to come. becuwse he were not well.

Furst we had to lern how to put up our tent. we wotcht mr jenkins demastrate and then we tryed adam took a foto off us when the tent was finaly up.

It was just then that it startid to rain. we all huddeled in our tent the rain kept comeing. it were geting werse and werse it was druming on the canvas and a huge puddel of warter forming on the roof of the tent suddenley a metel pole slipt and the tent collapset on top of us we was all sowkt The tent was recked what a mess

### Extra

Now write a diary entry for the next day.

## A Warm-up

Write two sentences for a story. Use one of these nouns in each sentence.

**farmer  tree**

1. _____

2. _____

3. Underline the odd one out.     *Clue: spelling*

   crying    dying    frying    spying

4. Give a reason for your choice.

   _____

   _____

5. Cross out the nouns. Write new nouns.

   **Smoke drifted in the air.**

   _____

Write three compound nouns starting with **water**.

6. water _____

7. water _____

8. water _____

Add the missing ending to make two rhyming words.

9. tunn _____    and    funn _____

10. junc _____    and    func _____

## B Word work

These words and prefixes are mixed up.
Write them correctly.

**un**behave **mis**obey **im**lucky **dis**possible

1. _____    3. _____

2. _____    4. _____

5. How do the prefixes change the meanings of the words?

   _____

6. What spelling rule do all these words follow?

   **machine  chalet  parachute**

   _____

7. Write another word that follows the same rule.

   _____

Write the meaning of the word in **bold**.

8. **settlement** _____

9. **population** _____

10. **locality** _____

## C Sentence work

Add the correct conjunction to complete the sentence.

**while  until  after  since**

1. Jack raced home _____ he escaped.

2. Someone had broken in _____ they were out.

3. They walked _____ they could go no further.

4. Jason had been an unusual child _____ he was born.

Underline the verb and change it to the present tense.

5. Leo lived on a faraway island. _____

6. Something was tapping on the window. _____

7. Emma and Rosita were friends. _____

Add the capital letters.

8. florence nightingale was born in florence in italy.

9. turn left into park street at simmond's supermarket.

10. i enjoyed 'snip snap', which is the new book by sam jackson.

18    Ⓧ There is only one correct answer.    Ⓧ There is more than one correct answer.

## A  Warm-up

1  Change the first clause in the sentence.

~~The wind howled~~ but I was safe in the hut.

_____

2  Write a sentence using these words.

**milk  but  cat**

_____

_____

3  The same letter is missing from all these words. Write it in.

_ i r c l e        _ e n t r e        _ y c l e

Add the missing syllable to complete the list of rhyming words.

4  tum_____        grum_____        rum_____

5  mud_____        pud_____         cud_____

6  bub_____        trou_____        stub_____

Add a word to make a compound noun.

7  heart_____        9  grape_____

8  wheel_____        10  horse_____

## B  Word work

Write the correct spelling.

1  skoolwork        _____

2  a ecko           _____

3  color sceme      _____

Underline the suffix that you can add to all the words. Write it in.

4  **ly  est  ful**

quick_____        ripe_____        kind_____

5  **ful  less  ly**

care_____         end_____         shame_____

6  **ly  less  er**

rich_____         like_____        final_____

Synonyms are words with similar meanings. Write two synonyms for the word in **bold**.

7  a **silly** idea      _____

8  a **fierce** beast    _____  _____

9  the **moody** boy     _____  _____

10  a **bright** light   _____  _____

## C  Sentence work

Cross out the phrase that starts with a preposition. Write a phrase starting with a different preposition.

1  A clown rode a unicycle down the road.        _____

2  The man jumped from a helicopter.             _____

3  The woman saw the dog by the shop.            _____

4  The ship sailed to the island.                _____

Add more to each instruction so it says exactly **where**. Use a preposition.

5  Sieve the flour _____

6  Bake the pie _____

7  Sprinkle sugar _____

What punctuation mark is hidden by the symbol?

▲We need biscuits■ eggs■ cereal and milk■ ▼ said Mum◆

8  ▲ ▼ =  _____

9  ■   =  _____

10  ◆   =  _____

X There is only one correct answer.    X There is more than one correct answer.

## A Warm-up

The beginnings and endings of these sentences are mixed up.

| | |
|---|---|
| **All books** | **is fiction.** |
| **Some books** | **have pages.** |
| **A storybook** | **has a glossary.** |
| **This book** | **are non-fiction.** |

Write the sentences correctly.

1 _____

2 _____

3 _____

4 _____

Make four compound nouns.    *Clue: clothing*

**suit sweat over pull track coat shirt**

5 _____    7 _____

6 _____    8 _____

Add the same missing letter to all three words.

9 ener_y    di_est    en_ine

10 re_ipe    pen_il    con_ert

## B Word work

Write the phrase so that the verb ends with **ing** and the noun is plural.

1 make jelly _____

2 drop catch _____

3 smile face _____

4 Add a prefix to make an opposite.

___ tidy        ___ honest

___ visible      ___ bug

Use the words in these sentences.

5 This room is _____ .

6 He had a _____ face.

7 The wizard made himself _____ .

8 We had to _____ the computer.

Write the meaning of the word in **bold**.

9 It was an **enchanting** evening.

'enchanting' means _____

10 He had to **obey** the king's wishes.

'obey' means _____

## C Sentence work

Add capital letters and full stops.

1 a fish is an animal with a tail and fins it lives in water

2 gently heat the mixture add the fruit stir until it is hot

3 the lights went out there was a thud someone screamed

Finish the sentence.

4 Bread goes crispy when _____

5 Your heart beats faster when _____

6 A bike stops when _____

Cross out the verb. Write a more interesting verb using the same tense.

7 He went through the brambles.

8 The monster was looking at him.

9 The thunder is banging.

10 Everyone ran away.

X There is only one correct answer.    X There is more than one correct answer.

## A Warm-up

1  Write the sentence using different nouns.

The burglar stole a painting
from the museum.

_____

Change one letter to make the word match
the meaning.

2  pour _____ means **not rich**

3  peak _____ means **to peep**

4  sun _____ means **a male child**

5  week _____ means **not strong**

Underline the word that is a synonym of the
word in **bold**.

6  **kind**   mean   cruel   caring   unkind

7  **strong**   weak   mighty   frail   feeble

8  **boring**   exciting   dull   thrilling

9  **ill**   untidy   sick   messy   well

10  The same syllable is missing from all these
words. Write it in.

v a n _____   p u n _____   a s t o n _____

## B Word work

1  Add the same prefix to all three words.

**un  re  de  dis**

___ play   ___ fill   ___ write

2  How does it change the meaning?

_____

3  Write two more words with this prefix.

_____   _____

Write two verbs that mean the same
as the verb in **bold**.

4  **laugh** _____ _____

5  **eat** _____ _____

6  **pull** _____ _____

7  **weep** _____ _____

Cross out the words that are wrongly spelt.
Write the correct spellings.

8  I herd two lorrys driveing around.

_____

9  A groop of childrun were droping litter.

_____

10  I notised it was offten cooler at night.

_____

## C Sentence work

Add the conjunction **after**, **when** or **until**.

1  We watched TV _____ it was bedtime.

2  We watched TV _____ we had tea.

3  We watched TV _____ we came in.

4  Underline the verbs in these instructions.

Add the banana. Beat with a wooden spoon. Empty the yoghurt into a bowl. Stir well.

5  What type of sentences are these? _____

Add **a** or **an**.

6  I had ___ apple ___ banana ___ orange and some grapes.

7  We saw ___ elephant ___ lion ___ anteater and some monkeys.

8  In my bag, I had ___ purse ___ umbrella ___ pen and some sweets.

9  In the garden, there was ___ oak tree ___ birch ___ willow and ___ elm.

10  What else is missing from these sentences? _____

X There is only one correct answer.   X There is more than one correct answer.

## A Warm-up

Change the second clause in the sentence.

1  Nathan and Sophie made a sandcastle ~~before they had an ice cream.~~

2  Marik began to run ~~when he saw the funfair.~~

These words and suffixes are mixed up.
Write them correctly.

**proper**ful **speech**ly **bead**less **wish**y

3 _____    5 _____

4 _____    6 _____

Add the missing vowel sound.

**ea  ee  ie  oa**

*Clue: used in place of said*

7  s q u ___ l e d    9  g r ___ n e d

8  s c r ___ c h e d   10  s h r ___ k e d

## B Word work

1  What do the words have in common?
**knack  wrong  gnarled  lamb**

2  What is the letter that is hidden?
▮nat  ▮naw  ▮nome  ▮nash

3  Add an **ed** ending.
**chuckle** _____    **cry** _____
**giggle** _____    **sob** _____

Write the new words as pairs of synonyms.

4  _____ and _____

5  _____ and _____

Write the meaning of the word in **bold**.

6  **disqualify** _____

7  **revisit** _____

8  **predict** _____

Sort the movement verbs.

**creep  thrash  crawl  scramble
scuttle  charge  drift  edge**

9  **slow** _____

10  **fast** _____

## C Sentence work

Add a conjunction to join the clauses. Do not use **and**.

1  Jack climbed _____ he reached the top.

2  It was dark _____ he took a torch.

3  The kite took off _____ the wind blew.

Underline the adjectives.

4  There was once a beautiful princess who lived in a sparkling palace on top of a high, misty mountain.

5  A thistle is a wild plant with purple flowers and prickly leaves.

6  Why are the adjectives used in the noun phrases?

Add the missing punctuation.

7  "can I come?" said the little girl

8  I can help you, said the mouse.

9  What are you doing said Jenny.

10  You shall go to the ball said the fairy godmother.

X There is only one correct answer.   X There is more than one correct answer.

## A   Warm-up

1. Extend the sentence so that it says **where** the prince ran.

   The prince ran _____

2. Add more so that it says **where** and **why**.

   The prince ran _____

   _____

Write four compound nouns ending with **ball**.
Write them in alphabetical order.

3. _____      5. _____

4. _____      6. _____

Underline the word that is **not** a synonym.

7. **shine**    gleam    fade    glint

8. **brave**    bold    daring    weak

9. **quick**    fast    fine    swift

10. The same vowel letter is missing from all these words. Write it in.

    g _ i d e      g _ e s s      g _ a r d

## B   Word work

1. Complete the word sum.

   1 **baby** × **2** = _____

   1 **child** × **2** = _____

   1 **mouse** × **2** = _____

   1 **man** × **2** = _____

2. Add **er** and **est**.

   **rich** _____ _____

   **pale** _____ _____

   **funny** _____ _____

Use one of the words you have made.

3. The Moon looks _____ than the Sun.

4. She told the _____ jokes.

5. He was the _____ man in the land.

6. The king was _____ than the beggar.

Add the missing vowels.

*Clue: found in food*

7. f _ b r _        9. v _ t _ m _ n s

8. c _ r b _ h y d r _ t e s    10. s _ g _ r

## C   Sentence work

Cross out the word that is wrong. Write the correct word.

1. Long ago, there lived an old man who has no money. _____

2. The princess stormed out of the palace and rides away. _____

3. The honey bee makes the honey we ate. _____

Add a list of three adjectives that describe the noun.

4. The hero was _____ _____ and _____ .

5. Try this _____ _____ _____ ice-cream.

6. He drove a _____ _____ _____ sports car.

Use the words to write one complete sentence.

7. **dragonfly**    insect    near water _____

8. **eel**    fish    long, thin _____

9. **holly**    evergreen    berries _____

10. **alligator**    reptile    swamps _____

X There is only one correct answer.    X There is more than one correct answer.    23

## A   Warm-up

The beginnings and endings of these sentences are mixed up.

**Some dogs**    moves round the Sun.
**Frogs**    dig holes.
**An artist**    eat flies.
**The Earth**    paints pictures.

Write the sentences correctly.

1 _____

2 _____

3 _____

4 _____

Underline the odd one out.

5   untrue  uniform  unfair  unlock  unreal

6   disagree  distrust  disallow  dishes  disorder

7   repay  reform  recycle  reread  really

8   Give a reason for your choices.

_____

Add a word to complete the longer word.

9   un _____ ful

10   dis _____ ing

## B   Word work

Add the missing syllable.

*Clue: buildings*

1   l i _____ r y

2   s u p _____ m a r

3   f a c _____ y

4   Add the suffix **ly** to make the word an adverb.

**sweet** _____

**safe** _____

**steady** _____

**easy** _____

Use one of these adverbs with each verb.

5   drive _____      7   rained _____

6   won _____      8   sang _____

Write the meaning of the word in **bold**.

9   The people were **alarmed** by the blaze.
'alarmed' means _____

10   The gates **prevent** him from entering.
'prevent' means _____

## C   Sentence work

Add words to the noun to make a longer, descriptive noun phrase.

1   **planet**     a _____ planet _____

2   **kitten**     the _____ kitten _____

3   **flower**     a _____ flower _____

4   **acrobat**     an _____ acrobat _____

Add the correct punctuation.

5   What  shall  we  do  asked  the  little  girl.

6   Who's  been  sitting  in  my  chair  said  Father  Bear.

7   Help  shouted  Jack.

Finish the sentence. Use a conjunction to add information that explains why.

8   Don't stand behind a moving swing

9   Eat lots of fruit and vegetables

10   We keep milk in a fridge

X There is only one correct answer.    X There is more than one correct answer.

## A Warm-up

1. Write a sentence using these words.

   **paint  but  ladder**

   _____

   _____

Add the missing letters.

**er  ir  ur**

*Clue: kinds of movement*

2. w h ___ l
3. s q u ___ m
4. c ___ l
5. j ___ k

6. Finish the sentence by giving a reason.

   The old man smiled _____

   _____

Add three letters to complete the word.

7. ___ c k l e
8. ___ c l e
9. ___ c e l
10. ___ c i l

## B Word work

Make an adjective from the word in **bold** and use it to complete the sentence.

1. A bear has **fur**. It is _____ .
2. The silver coin **shines**. It is _____ .
3. He drove in the **fog**. It was _____ .
4. There is a **haze**. It is _____ .

5. All these words have the same spelling pattern.

   **myth  gym  crystal**

   What is the pattern?

   _____

Write three more words with the same pattern.

6. E g ___ t
7. p ___ r ___ m ___ d
8. m ___ s t ___ y

Write two antonyms (opposites) for the word in **bold**.

9. The prince was **kind**.

   _____

10. The shop was **neat**.

    _____

## C Sentence work

Cross out the nouns and write them as plurals. Write the new sentence so that it makes sense.

1. Waiting inside was a woman with a baby and a schoolchild.

   Waiting inside _____

2. The old lady had a bad foot. _____

Add another clause to complete the sentence.

3. The party went well until _____
4. As he made his wish, _____

Add the full stops and capital letters.

5. a plant is a living thing it has a stem, leaves and roots most plants grow in the earth
6. march is the third month it has 31 days it is named after the roman god mars
7. it was late dylan had not come home sadiq and bella were waiting for him

Cross out the phrase that starts with a preposition. Write a phrase starting with a different preposition.

8. The old man kept watch during the night. _____
9. The little boy hid in the corner. _____
10. The thieves climbed into the house. _____

## A Warm-up

1. Underline the word that is **not** an adjective.

smooth   rough   rock   hard   powdery

2. Add a suffix to make it an adjective.

_____ + _____ = _____

3. Add a suffix to make this word into an adjective.

**beauty** _____

Change the verb to make a new sentence.

**He smiled at the boy.**

4. _____

5. _____

Write four compound words that start with **under**.

6. under _____   8. under _____

7. under _____   9. under _____

10. The same two-letter word fits into all these longer words. Write it in.

c _ tinue    sec _ d    _ ce

## B Word work

Add two different suffixes.

1. **crazy** _____

2. **flat** _____

3. **kind** _____

4. **gentle** _____

Write the meaning of the word in **bold**.

5. This paper is **absorbent**.

'absorbent' means _____

6. The glass is **transparent**.

'transparent' means _____

7. The plastic is **opaque**.

'opaque' means _____

Cross out the words that are wrongly spelt. Write the correct spellings.

8. I desided to rest for a minite.

_____  _____

9. Imajine a stranje land.

_____  _____

10. I'm sertain that cherrys taste grate.

## C Sentence work

Rewrite each pair of sentences as one sentence. Use an adverb in place of the second sentence.

1. He turned away. He was sad.

2. He faced the tiger. He was brave.

3. He folded the clothes. They were neat.

4. Underline the adjectives.

The alien had an enormous head with round, bulging eyes. Its tiny body was covered in red, pointed scales. It had a short, brownish tail with a green tuft on the end.

Write each adjective beside the type of thing it describes.

5. **colour** _____  _____

6. **size** _____  _____

7. **shape** _____  _____

Complete the sentence so that it says **when** the event happened. Use a conjunction.

8. Abdul had a slice of apple pie _____

9. The farmer became rich _____

10. The snow melted _____

X There is only one correct answer.   X There is more than one correct answer.

English Skills 1

## A Warm-up

**1** Add the suffix **y** to make an adjective.

**powder** _____

**gloss** _____

**dust** _____

**shine** _____

Write the words as pairs of synonyms.

**2** _____ and _____

**3** _____ and _____

Add the missing vowels.    **Clue:** *conjunctions*

**4** b f r

**5** b c s

**6** s n c

**7** n t l

**8** Write a sentence using these words.

**mouse   when   cat**

_____

_____

Use a preposition to add more to the sentence.

**We played chess.**

**9** _____

**10** _____

## B Word work

**1** Add the same missing letter to all three words.

s _ i e n c e       s _ e n e

s _ i s s o r s     f a s _ i n a t e

Add the missing syllable.

**2** d i f _ e n t

**4** i m _ t a n t

**3** i n _ i g e n t

**5** r e _ b e r

**6** Add the same suffix to all the words.

**ful  ly  ness  less**

friend _____    real _____    actual _____

**7** Use two of the words in this sentence.

The new boy was _____ .

Write three synonyms for the word in **bold**.

**8** **pretty** _____

**9** **sly** _____

**10** **scary** _____

## C Sentence work

Add the punctuation and capital letters.

**1** who  wants  an  ice-cream  asked  melanie

**2** me  screamed  bobbie  and  robbie

**3** what  flavour  do  you  want  there  is  mint  or  vanilla  explained  melanie

Rewrite the sentence as a command.

**4** We had to beat the eggs with a fork.

**5** The milk and sugar were added to the eggs.

**6** We baked it for 25 minutes.

Continue the sentence after the conjunction.

**7** Martha had very little money so

**8** Martha had very little money because

**9** Martha had very little money until

**10** Martha had very little money since

X There is only one correct answer.    X There is more than one correct answer.

## A  Warm-up

Continue the sentence. Use two prepositions.

1  The ball bounced _____

_____

2  The boy slipped _____

_____

Make three words using these
letters only.

**e i d t**

3  _____  **Clue:** *changes in sea level*

4  _____  **Clue:** *the food you eat*

5  _____  **Clue:** *made a knot*

Add a short word to complete the longer word.

6  t o ___ h e r       8  s u d ___ l y

7  b e ___ v e       9  s e n ___ c e

10  Add the same vowel sound to all the words.

**or  ea  ear  air**

s ___ c h       t h ___       l y ___

## B  Word work

Complete the word sums.

1  **greed + y =** _____  **+ est =** _____
2  **sun + y =** _____  **+ est =** _____
3  **skin + y =** _____  **+ est =** _____
4  **scare + y =** _____  **+ est =** _____

Write three nouns that name types of

5  **aircraft** _____
6  **storm** _____
7  **bird** _____

Write the pairs of words
with the same spelling pattern.
Add another similar word.

**double  wand  couple  wash**

8  _____ , _____ and _____
9  _____ , _____ and _____

10  Cross out the words that are wrongly spelt.
Write the correct spellings.

Carefully slice strawberrys into quorters.

_____

## C  Sentence work

Add the missing words to the dialogue. It begins, **"When will we see the sea?" asked Jamie.**

1  _____ replied Dad.

2  _____ shouted Jamie excitedly.

Rewrite the sentence so that it says **where** and **when** the event happened. Use two prepositions.

3  Jacob went shopping.

_____

4  There was a fire.

_____

5  I met George.

_____

Underline the word that is incorrect. Write it correctly.

6  I visit my dad every Sunday and he took me out.
7  The farmer ran and hides behind a nearby rock.
8  The wizard was sitting and writes in his book of spells.
9  The prince stops and grabbed his sword.
10  The girl saw the old lady but she says nothing.

X There is only one correct answer.    X There is more than one correct answer.

## A Warm-up

Cross out the nouns. Write a new sentence with different nouns.

1. A bull has horns.

_____

2. Tom was an elf who lived in a wood.

_____

Underline the correct spelling.

3. yung    yong    young

4. ankor    anchor    ancor

5. gymnast    gimnast    jymnast

Add different prefixes to the word **cover** to make three new words.

6. ____ cover

7. ____ cover

8. ____ cover

9. Underline the word that is not a compound word.

without  inside  something  follow  anyone

10. Give a reason for your choice.

_____

## B Word work

1. Add the silent consonant.

s _ o r d          i _ l a n d

g _ o s t          a n s _ e r

2. Add the suffix **less** to form adjectives. Some letters may need to be crossed out.

worth _____          penny _____

use _____          tire _____

Use the words in these noun phrases.

3. a _____ beggar

4. a _____ tool

5. a _____ painting

6. a _____ worker

7. Add the vowels.  *Clue: weather*

c l _ m _ t _    d r _    _ g h t    t _ r n _ d

Use the words in these sentences.

8. A _____ tore up the trees.

9. We have a mild _____ .

10. There may soon be a _____ .

## C Sentence work

1. Write a sentence for a story using a preposition and a conjunction.

The little frog _____

2. Write a sentence for a report using a preposition and a conjunction.

A frog _____

Complete the sentence using the words **a**, **an**, **the**.

3. There was _____ empty box and _____ large suitcase in _____ middle of Greg's room.

4. _____ red car had _____ dent and made _____ awful noise but it was _____ best price.

Add adjectives to complete the noun phrases.

5. The house was _____ and _____ with a _____ door and an _____ garden.

6. The _____ man had a _____ face with _____ eyes.

7. The sky was _____ with _____ clouds covering the _____ moon.

Add the capital letters and punctuation.

8. our  senses  allow  us  to  see  feel  taste  hear  and  smell  things.

9. i  must  warn  king  louis  said  ivan.

10. dont  do  it  shouted  maria.

**Now complete Section 2 of the Progress chart on page 46.**

X There is only one correct answer.    X There is more than one correct answer.

## Dressed for the weather

Write three or four paragraphs for an information text called **Dressed for the weather**. You should give information about what clothes to wear in different countries or at different times of year.

### Hints

Before you start, think about:

- the information you want to give
- how you will organise your writing.

As you write, think about:

- the words you choose
- the sentences you write.

### Check

- When you have finished, check through your writing.
- Check that everything sounds right.
- Proofread to check spelling and punctuation.
- Make changes to improve it.

## The lost treasure

Proofread this story.

Change anything that does not look or sound correct.

### Hints

- Check that everything is clear and sounds right.
- Check that the punctuation and capital letters are correct.
- Check that the spelling is correct.

The stoney path twistid up into the mowntains there was a fearfull rumbul far away that went eckoing across the vally Clara was glad she had her map sord and her fathers majic cloak with her. they wuld help protect her from truble

Clara scrambuld up the steep path untill she was lost in the mists she used her hands to gide her until suddunley the path became flata. the mist cleered in a few minites and clara was standin at the edje of the bigist cave she had ever seen. She creeps closer And peers inside.

Just at that moment she herd a mightey roar and a powerfull voyce. Who dares come to the cave of zog? it cryed.

### Extra

Now write an ending for the story. Think carefully about the words and sentences you use.

```



```

## A  Warm-up

Add the missing letters. *Clue: shapes*

① ☐ i r ☐ ☐

② h e x ☐ g o n

③ r e ☐ t ☐ g ☐ ☐

④ c ☐ l ☐ d

Finish the sentence.

⑤ The monster ate _____

⑥ He lived in a cave _____

⑦ He roared _____

⑧ The monster was sad _____

Sort the words into two sets of synonyms.

**sturdy  weak  powerful  feeble**

**powerless  frail  burly  strong**

⑨ _____

⑩ _____

## B  Word work

① What spelling pattern do these words share?

**creature  texture  adventure**

_____

Write four more words with the same pattern.

② _____    ④ _____

③ _____    ⑤ _____

Add a suffix to each word so you can use it in one of the sentences.

**sense  amaze**

⑥ I felt a strange _____ .

⑦ He looked round in _____ .

Write three synonyms of the word in **bold**.

⑧ The man wore **nice** clothes.

_____    _____

⑧ The burglar **went** up the path.

_____    _____

⑩ There was a **sound** of machinery.

_____    _____

## C  Sentence work

Improve the verb in the sentence. Cross out the verb and write a more interesting one.

① Some animals sleep in winter.

② Mrs Hawkins is giving the prizes.

③ Carefully, stick on the wheels.

④ The angry man went out the door.

Write the sentence as direct speech.

⑤ Ben asked his mum for help.

⑥ Josh shouted hello to Ravi.

⑦ Katie asked the time.

⑧ Add the capital letters and full stops.

   emily turned there was a wolf he was standing right behind her

⑨ Rewrite the sentences above as one complete sentence using a conjunction.

⑩ Write another sentence that says what happened next. Use a different conjunction.

Ⓧ There is only one correct answer.    Ⓧ There is more than one correct answer.

## A  Warm-up

1  Add the same missing letter to all three words.

c r e s _ e n t  s _ e n t e d  s _ e n e r y

Make four words using these words and suffixes only.

**cheer  quiet  ful  ness  er  y**

2  _____  4  _____

3  _____  5  _____

The beginnings and endings of these sentences are mixed up.

| **Fish** | work in schools. |
| **Teachers** | bark loudly. |
| **Some dogs** | have humps. |
| **Camels** | live in water. |

Write the sentences correctly.

6  _____

7  _____

8  _____

9  _____

10  Make two words using these letters only.

a r w  _____  and  _____

## B  Word work

1  What root word do all these words share?

**actor  active  reaction  activity**

Write four more words from this word family.

2  _____  4  _____

3  _____  5  _____

Write a synonym of the word in **bold**.

6  He was a **troublesome** boy.

7  That's **precisely** what I meant.

8  He was **dumbfounded**.

Sort the words into two groups.

**caring  thoughtful  heartless  spiteful**

**unfeeling  ruthless  considerate  unselfish**

9  **kind** _____

10  **cruel** _____

## C  Sentence work

Complete the sentence. Add commas where they are needed.

1  Yasmin shut the front door locked it put the key in her bag and _____

2  Tom stamped his feet flung down his bag screwed up his face and _____

3  The magician stood up waved his wand said the magic words and _____

Use one of these subordinating conjunctions to complete the sentence.  **if  since  although**

4  I like playing football _____ I'm not that good at it.

5  We have lived here _____ I was five.

6  I know I will do it _____ I keep trying.

Underline the phrase that says **why** the king left.

7  The king was forced to leave his castle because of the ice monsters.

Complete the sentence with a phrase starting with a preposition to say **why**.

8  The family left in a hurry _____

9  Great Western Street is closed _____

10  My bus was late _____

X There is only one correct answer.  X There is more than one correct answer.

## A Warm-up

1 Write a sentence using these nouns.

**giant  flower  garden**

_____

_____

Add the missing letters.

*Clue: parts of your hand*

2 w r _____   4 k n _____

3 t h _____

5 Make two compound nouns that use any of the words above.

_____

Add the missing letters.

**er  ear  ir  ur**

6 t h _____ s t y   8 m i s h _____ d

7 p _____ p o s e   9 a d v _____ b

Use a conjunction to add more information.

10 Ruby remembered the stranger _____

## B Word work

Write four words that belong to the same word family as **happy**.

1 _____   3 _____

2 _____   4 _____

Add the correct verb endings.

5 We went swim _____ , sunbathe _____ and paddle _____ .

6 They came run _____ , skid _____ and hurtle _____ into the playground.

7 Write a synonym of the adverb in **bold**.

**gruffly** _____

**immensely** _____

**gleefully** _____

Add the missing ending.

8 There is a road clo _____ ahead.

9 The invaders cap _____ the castle.

10 Write a cap _____ for the picture.

## C Sentence work

Add the punctuation and capital letters.

1 mr marshall found a dusty old picture in his house in lexton somerset

2 was it worth anything the answer is yes

3 mr marshall told our reporter, I was most surprised to hear it was valuable

Underline the subordinate clause.

4 The man's eyes flashed as he glared at Simon.   5 He stomped around while he raged.

6 What do these sentences tell us about the character? _____

Add a subordinate clause to match the new mood of the character.

7 The man's eyes twinkled _____

8 He danced around _____

Rewrite the information in one sentence.

9 Stir the mixture. Use a wooden spoon. Stop when it is golden brown.

_____

10 A bat is a small animal. It looks like a mouse. It has wings.

_____

X There is only one correct answer.   X There is more than one correct answer.

## A  Warm-up

These words and suffixes are mixed up.
Write them correctly.

good**less**  hair**ful**  regret**ness**

① _____    ③ _____

② _____

Add a main clause.

④  While she waited, _____

⑤  As darkness fell, _____

Add the missing letters.

**oar  au  ar**

⑥ c l ___ s e        ⑧ s w ___ m e d

⑦ s ___ e d

Cross out the verbs and write new ones.

⑨  They strolled down the road,
    laughing and joking.
    _____

⑩  Trees whispered and waved in the wind.
    _____

## B  Word work

Write the words as contractions.

①  **does not**   _____

②  **she has**    _____

③  **I would**    _____

④  **will not**   _____

⑤  Underline the prefix.

   disconnect    misplace    rearrange

Write a definition (the meaning) of the word.

⑥  **disconnect**  _____

⑦  **misplace**    _____

⑧  **rearrange**   _____

Sort the words into two word families.

**century  circus  centimetre
circular  circle  centipede**

⑨ _____

⑩ _____

## C  Sentence work

Write in the missing word.

**his  her  our  their**

①  The lady put _____ bag on the floor.

②  The children told the teacher _____ story.

③  Joe spoke to _____ best friend.

④  We wrote _____ names at the top.

Write the sentence, adding the missing apostrophe.

⑤  The doctors looked at Georges X-rays.

⑥  The mans hands were shaking.

⑦  Cracks appeared in the Earths surface.

Continue the sentence about a story you have read.

⑧  I have chosen this story because _____

⑨  You will enjoy this story if _____

⑩  I liked the story although _____

Ⓧ There is only one correct answer.    Ⓧ There is more than one correct answer.

35

## A  Warm-up

Add a short word to complete the longer word.

**1** o r ____ a r y  **3** c h a r ____ e r

**2** i n t e ____ i n g  **4** c o n ____ u e

**5** Use these words to make five compound words.

**in  out  ways  with  side**

_____

_____

Add an adjective to the sentence.

**6** The hare was _____ than the tortoise.

**7** A book is _____ than a feather.

**8** A mango is _____ than an apple.

**9** Mars is _____ than the Sun

but _____ than the Moon.

**10** Write a sentence using these verbs.

**snarled  wriggled**

_____

_____

## B  Word work

Add the correct ending so the word matches the definition.

**1** trea _____ gold and jewels

**2** den _____ false teeth

**3** furni _____ tables and chairs

**4** plea _____ happiness

Change the nouns into plurals.

**5** The leaf fluttered on the branch.

_____

**6** We took the loaf off the shelf.

_____

**7** The furry bunny rode in the buggy.

_____

Use one of these words in the sentence.

**structure  inflatable  reclaimed**

**8** This airbed is _____ .

**9** We built a tall _____ .

**10** We used _____ materials.

## C  Sentence work

Add punctuation to the direct speech.

**1** Have you remembered the box asked Julia.

**2** We are nearly there said Umar.

**3** That's it shouted Nick Let's go

**4** Be careful Its very icy warned Joe.

Use one of these adverbs to complete the sentence.

**afterwards  suddenly  eventually**

**5** It was a long journey but they arrived _____ .

**6** We watched the match and _____ we had tea.

**7** They fell asleep until _____ the phone rang.

Improve the report by changing the words in **bold**. Write the sentence with the new words in place.

**8** We **got** the rainwater in the **pot**.

**9** Then we can **see how much rain there is**.

**10** We **put** the **numbers** on a **paper**.

X There is only one correct answer.  X There is more than one correct answer.

## A  Warm-up

Write four nouns ending with **ness**.

1 _____   3 _____

2 _____   4 _____

5 Add the correct double consonant.

h o ___ l e

g r a ___ ___ a r

r o ___ ___ e n

Continue the sentence.

6 King Crumble was happy if _____

7 King Crumble was happy because _____

8 King Crumble was happy until _____

9 King Crumble was happy so _____

10 King Crumble was happy though _____

## B  Word work

Add the same ending.

1 televi _____

2 confu _____

3 comprehen _____

4 Write another word with the same ending.

_____

Write the sentence correctly.

5 I beleve we breath in oxijen.

_____

6 Ive choosen my favrite color.

_____

7 I surpose you are to bizy to come.

_____

Write an adjective that is stronger than the word in **bold**.

8 It was a **horrible** sight. _____

9 The book was **interesting**. _____

10 She was **surprised**. _____

## C  Sentence work

Add a comma.

1 Food helps us to grow gives us energy and keeps us healthy.

Add three phrases to complete the sentence.

2 An elephant uses its trunk to _____

3 Seeds are dispersed by _____

Add **has** or **have** to complete the perfect form of the verb.

4 You _____ won first prize!

5 This year Dad _____ planted lots of vegetables in the garden.

6 I _____ been fishing once before.

Which of these adverbs show time and which show place?

**next  outside  here  today  meanwhile  everywhere**

7 time _____        8 place _____

Continue the sentence after the adverb.

9 The shadowy figure disappeared but later _____

10 Sieve the flour into the bowl and next _____

X There is only one correct answer.    X There is more than one correct answer.

## A Warm-up

Write an antonym.

1. inflate
2. input
3. equal

Write each singular noun as a plural.

4. puppy     kitten     mouse

5. prince     princess     wolf

Add a reason for the event.

6. He waited outside the bank

7. He opened the chest carefully

Add the missing letters.

*Clue: they are all directions*

8. f    w    d s    10. c l    w    e

9. b    w    d s

## B Word work

1. Complete the word sum.

   **scurry + ed** =

   **plenty + ful** =

   **hungry + ly** =

   **steady + ness** =

2. What spelling rule did you use?

Write the verb beside the correct definition.

**construct examine increase magnify**

3. _____ look at closely
4. _____ enlarge
5. _____ build
6. _____ add to/make larger

Add the same prefix to all three words.

7. freeze    septic    clockwise
8. read    behave    understand
9. man    star    store
10. val    view    city

## C Sentence work

Add the missing punctuation and capital letters.

1. dear mrs jenkins

   you are a winner you have won first prize in our competition

2. hi joss

   we will meet you and andy at penley station on saturday see you then

3. dear mr clarke

   i greatly enjoyed your book 'cold times' you are my favourite author

Complete the sentence so it has a main clause and a subordinate clause.

4. The children of Class 4
5. The message
6. A shadow
7. The lion

Cross out the words that do not sound right. Write the correct words.

8. "I is hungry," said the alien. "What does you eat on you planet?"
9. "I likes it here. Everyone are very friendy to my."
10. "I thinks there is lots more peoples for I to meet."

X There is only one correct answer.    X There is more than one correct answer.

## A　Warm-up

Write a sentence using these words.

1　**moon　dog　street**

2　**water　park　kite**

Write the adjective ending with **less**.

3　_____ less　　*Clue: not scared*

4　_____ less　　*Clue: cannot speak*

5　_____ less　　*Clue: gasping for air*

Sort the adverbs into two groups.

**just then,　finally,　later,**

**now,　eventually,　suddenly**

6　**in the end**

7　**right then**

Complete the word chain.

**cold　colder　coldest**

8　hot

9　close

10　heavy

## B　Word work

Write a definition of the word in **bold**.

1　We went on a **train**.

　　**train:**

2　We **train** daily for the race.

　　**train:**

3　She put the **ring** on her finger.

　　**ring:**

4　A bell began to **ring**.

　　**ring:**

5　What do you notice about the words **train** and **ring**?

Write the word with the apostrophe in the correct place. Then write the full form.

6　**shell'**

7　**well'**

8　**were'**

9　**shed'**

10　**youd**

## C　Sentence work

Write these lines so that the **said** part is in the middle of the dialogue, not at the end.

1　"What are you doing here? This is private land," said the man.

2　"I am Zoll. I come from the planet Kroll," said the alien.

3　"Come here, Sophie. I want to speak to you," said Mum.

Make the character sound angry. Write a verb to use instead of **said**.

4　_____ the man

5　_____ the alien

6　_____ Mum

Write the sentence using the present perfect form of the verb.

7　I lost my glasses.

8　I looked everywhere for them.

9　Mum searched the car.

10　No-one found them.

## A  Warm-up

Change the nouns so the sentence gives a different picture.

1. A man stood by the door holding a briefcase.

_____

2. The fox followed the chicken into the farmyard.

_____

3. The baker put the cake in the oven.

_____

Add **s** or **c** to complete the word.

4. n o t i _ e          6. c o n v i n _ e

5. p r o m i _ e        7. i n c r e a _ e

Underline the two words in each list that have more than one meaning.

8. ice  spot  day  chin  bat

9. light  ear  wave  flour  big

10. rose  frog  leaves  grass  bud

## B  Word work

Complete these word sums.

1. **sudden + ness =** _____

2. **plain   + ness =** _____

3. Underline the prefix.

   subway   submarine

4. What does the prefix mean?

   _____

Add the suffix **ation** to these verbs.

5. inform _____    7. tempt _____

6. invite _____    8. examine _____

9. What type of word have you made? Tick one.

   verb       adjective       noun       adverb

10. Add the missing syllables.
    *Clue: finding and thinking*
    d i s ___ e r i n g     c o n ___ e r i n g

## C  Sentence work

Cross out the past tense verb. Rewrite the sentence using the perfect form.

1. I ate my lunch already.

2. We raised lots of money so far.

3. My sunflower grew 2cm since yesterday.

4. I was here before.

5. Check the punctuation. Add two full stops and two exclamation marks.

   SLAM Everyone stood very still Yes, it was a magic carpet No-one moved for a long time

6. Why did you decide to use exclamation marks where you did?

   _____

7. Underline the main clause in the sentence.

   While everyone slept, the snow began to fall.

Finish the sentence by adding a subordinate clause.

8. The town turned into a magical place

9. The people saw the smooth, unmarked snow

10. The water had frozen

X There is only one correct answer.     X There is more than one correct answer.

### A  Warm-up

Finish the second sentence.

1. Jack searched for the gold. Before long,

2. Jack searched for the gold. Meanwhile,

Write two synonyms for the word in **bold**.

3. **shake**

4. **hungry**

5. **creep**

Add the missing letters.

*Clue: school subjects*

6. h i ___ ___ y

7. s ___ ___ c e

8. g e o ___ ___ ___ y

9. c o m ___ ___ i n g

10. Write a sentence using these words.

    **cat  bowl  suitcase**

### B  Word work

Write a definition of the word in **bold**.

1. They began to **row** down the river.

2. We put out a **row** of chairs.

3. There was a terrible **row** afterwards.

What do you notice about the word **row**?

4. 

5. 

These words and suffixes are
mixed up. Write them correctly.

**shopness  readyful  painer**

6. ___          8. ___

7. ___

Correct the spelling.

9. Purhaps peeple shuld laff moore.

10. Exersize is realy good for the hart.

### C  Sentence work

Continue the sentence with a subordinate clause.

1. Plants will not grow unless

2. Houseplants do not grow outside because

3. Protect your outdoor plants if

4. Underline the adverb in the sentence below.

   The van raced down the high street, swerving everywhere and stopping the traffic.

5. What does the adverb tell you?

Write a sentence about a van using the two adverbs in bold.

6. **soon      here**

7. **later     away**

Add the capital letters and punctuation to the direct speech.

8. climb up here said the snake it is quite safe

9. what's that asked the farmer is it gold

10. oh thank you sobbed the girl

X There is only one correct answer.      X There is more than one correct answer.

41

## A  Warm-up

Underline the word that is **not** a real word.

1. careless   tuneless   tiredless   homeless
2. likely   really   mostly   leastly
3. villager   officer   schooler   driver

Continue the sentence so that it explains **why**.

4. She was excited

5. He dashed out of the house

6. The Moon is different from the Earth

Add a short word to complete the longer word.

7. ___ t e n
8. a l ___ g
9. s o ___ t i m e s
10. b e c a ___ e

## B  Word work

1. Write the prefix beside its definition.
   **auto  pre  anti**

   ___  self or own
   ___  against
   ___  before

Write two words starting with the prefix.

2. **auto**
3. **pre**
4. **anti**

Write two different definitions.

5. **gum**

6. **fit**

7. **pop**

Complete the pairs of homophones.

8. cheap and c h ___
9. meet and m ___
10. seen and s ___

## C  Sentence work

Add a conjunction to link the two clauses.

1. "I did it ___ I thought you would be pleased."
2. "We can try ___ I'm not very hopeful."
3. "Let's tidy up ___ Mum is out."

Add the capital letters and punctuation.

4. buzzz what was that it was too loud to be a fly what could it be
5. they shouted no-one came they shouted again but still no-one came
6. it was a great big elephant an elephant in their front garden

Write the sentence again using at least one longer noun phrase.

7. The woman carried a box.

8. The castle was made of bricks and had five turrets.

9. He wore a hat and a cloak.

10. How do the noun phrases improve the sentences?

X There is only one correct answer.   X There is more than one correct answer.

## A  Warm-up

Finish the sentence.

1 Matt did not listen because

2 Matt did not listen when

3 Matt did not listen until

Use the same word to complete both phrases.

4 wrist _____     _____ dog

5 traffic _____     toast and _____

6 _____ for sale     _____ as a pancake

7 The same vowel letters are missing from all these words. Write them in.

| y ___ n g | c ___ s i n |
| c ___ n t r y | t ___ c h |

Complete the word to match the definition.

8 mis _____     bad luck

9 dis _____     vanish

10 in _____     not finished

## B  Word work

Use the prefixes and suffixes to make four words that belong to the same word family as **fold**.

**un  re  er  able**

1 _____     3 _____

2 _____     4 _____

Use two of the words you have made.

5 This box is _____ .

6 I'll fold it and then _____ it.

Write a definition of the word in **bold**.

7 This box is **recyclable**.

8 The door is **unhinged**.

Underline the words that are wrongly spelt. Write the correct spellings.

9 Make shure the adress is writen clearley.

10 Do you surve enuff froot joose?

## C  Sentence work

Complete the subordinate clause.

1 As _____ , Mack began to smile.

2 If _____ , it would be too late.

3 Before _____ , the classroom door flew open.

4 When _____ , he found Marie already waiting.

Complete the sentence using prepositions, adverbs or conjunctions to add interesting detail.

5 The children rushed

6 The princess peered

7 The sheepdog ran

Proofread the text and write it correctly.

8 two mouses appeared squeak squeak they said

9 help screamed Jo climbing on the chair

10 felix the cat drinked the kittens milk

**Now complete Section 3 of the Progress chart on page 46.**

X There is only one correct answer.    X There is more than one correct answer.

43

# WRITING TASK 3

## Adventure story

Write an exciting opening for an adventure story.

### Hints

Before you start:

- choose a title for your story – either **Mystery Towers** or **The Disappearing Box**
- write the title at the top of the box below
- think about an exciting event to start off your story
- think about what makes an adventure story sound exciting.

As you write, think about:

- the words you choose
- the sentences you write.

Title:

### Check

- When you have finished, check through your writing.
- Check that everything sounds right.
- Proofread to check spelling and punctuation.
- Make changes to improve it.

44

## Letter to the head

Proofread this letter from Class G to their head teacher.

Change anything that does not look or sound correct.

### Hints

- Check that everything is clear and sounds right.
- Check that the punctuation and capital letters are correct.
- Check that the spelling is correct.

Deer  mrs  jenkins

We  are  riteing  to  tell  you  about  our  sceme  for  raiseing  muney  to  by  the  new  playgrownd  equipmunt  we  have  desided  to  hold  a  plant  sale  we  will  grow  a  mixtcher  of  plants  from  seed  and  then  sell  them  we  will  put  all  the  informashun  on  the  scools  website  so  pairents  can  read  it.

We  beleeve  it  is  a  really  good  idea  becuse  we  can  grow  the  plants  as  part  of  our  sciense  project  did  I  menshun  we  has  been  lerning  how  plants  grow.  we  will  only  need  a  few  packits  of  seeds  some  pots  and  some  compost.  That  will  be  enuff  to  begin  with.

We  hopes  you  find  our  idea  intresting.

Class  g

### Extra

Write another very short letter to the head. Choose a different idea.

# ENGLISH SKILLS 1 | Progress chart

Name: _____     Class/Set: _____

Teacher's name: _____     Date: _____

## Instructions

Read the **'I can' targets** for the section you have just finished.
- Colour the circle **green** if you find it **easy** to do what is described.
- Colour the circle **orange** if you are **getting there**, but still need to work on it.
- Colour the circle **red** if you still find this a **difficult** thing to do.

If there are things that you still find difficult, you can work on them in the next section or in the next book.

## Writing sentences

| 'I can' targets | Section 1 | Section 2 | Section 3 |
|---|---|---|---|
| I can write statements, questions, commands and exclamations. | ○ | ○ | ○ |
| I can use **and**, **but** and **or** to join words or ideas in sentences. | ○ | ○ | ○ |
| I can write sentences using conjunctions like **because**, **if** and **since**. | ○ | ○ | ○ |
| I can use conjunctions, adverbs and prepositions to add detail. | | ○ | ○ |
| I can use longer noun phrases to add description or important detail. | | ○ | ○ |

## Using punctuation

| | Section 1 | Section 2 | Section 3 |
|---|---|---|---|
| I can use capital letters and full stops to start and end sentences. | ○ | ○ | ○ |
| I can use **?** and **!** when they are needed. | ○ | ○ | ○ |
| I can use commas in lists of nouns and phrases. | ○ | ○ | ○ |
| I can use capital letters for names and titles. | ○ | ○ | ○ |
| I can use apostrophes to show possession. | ○ | ○ | ○ |
| I can use inverted commas and punctuate direct speech. | | ○ | ○ |

## Checking grammar

| | Section 1 | Section 2 | Section 3 |
|---|---|---|---|
| I can write in past or present tense. | ○ | ○ | ○ |
| I can check that the verbs in my sentences are correct. | ○ | ○ | ○ |
| I can choose precise nouns, verbs and adjectives. | ○ | ○ | ○ |
| I can use **an** instead of **a** before a word beginning with a vowel. | | ○ | ○ |
| I can use present perfect verb forms. | | | ○ |

## Understanding and choosing words

| | Section 1 | Section 2 | Section 3 |
|---|---|---|---|
| I can suggest words with similar meanings. | ○ | ○ | ○ |
| I can work out the meaning of a word from how it is used. | ○ | ○ | ○ |
| I can work out meaning by looking at the parts of a word. | ○ | ○ | ○ |
| I can use prefixes to change the meaning of words. | ○ | ○ | ○ |
| I can use suffixes to change words into nouns, adjectives or adverbs. | ○ | ○ | ○ |
| I can suggest words that belong in the same word family. | | | ○ |

## Spelling

| | Section 1 | Section 2 | Section 3 |
|---|---|---|---|
| I can segment words and choose the correct spelling for sounds. | ○ | ○ | ○ |
| I can spell longer words including endings (e.g. **ture**, **sure**, **tion**, **sion**). | ○ | ○ | ○ |
| I can spell tricky words such as **guard**, **circle** and **February**. | ○ | ○ | ○ |
| I can spell words using prefixes (**un**, **dis**) and suffixes (**ful**, **ly**). | ○ | ○ | ○ |
| I can use the rules for adding suffixes (e.g. **happiness**). | ○ | ○ | ○ |
| I can use the rules to spell plurals. | ○ | ○ | ○ |
| I can choose the correct spelling of homophones (e.g. **mail**, **male**). | ○ | ○ | ○ |
| I can spell words with unusual spelling patterns (e.g. **school**, **myth**, **echo**). | | ○ | ○ |
| I can use apostrophes in contractions (e.g. **can't**). | | | ○ |